D1007883

I CAN'T SLEEP

KNOCK
KNOCK®
VENICE, CALIFORNIA

Created, published, and distributed by Knock Knock
1635-B Electric Ave.
Venice, CA 90291
knockknockstuff.com
Knock Knock is a registered trademark of Knock Knock LLC
Inner-Truth is a trademark of Knock Knock LLC

ISBN: 978-160106343-4
UPC: 825703-50077-6

30 29

YOU'RE STILL
AWAKE

It's no wonder. With so much stuff requiring your obsessive consideration every single day, who could possibly blame you?

Whether you're preoccupied with finances, matters of the heart, life goals, or the innumerable errands that should have been run last week, when the clock strikes midnight—or 3:00 AM—taming those wild thoughts can be a Herculean task.

Although you may toil through the night by yourself, you're not alone—insomnia affects tens of millions of people. According to the Mayo Clinic, more than a third of adults have sleep-related issues at one point or another, and 10 to 15 percent are chronic insomniacs. The National Sleep Foundation found that only 28 percent of us get the full eight hours that experts recommend.

Naturally, insomnia's causes are as varied as its sufferers, ranging from psychological problems (stress, depression, or anxiety) to illness (hormonal imbalance, aches and pains, or just a stuffy nose), to environmental factors (a heavy dinner, living above a nightclub, or a snoring partner). While sleep deprivation has well-documented negative effects, including mental fogginess and weight gain, it also has potential upsides. Sleep researcher Jerome Siegel says insomnia may be nature's way of improving our time management; we sleep only when we need to and are awake when we're most inclined to be productive. Perhaps not surprisingly, studies have also found that night owls are, in fact, more intelligent than early risers.

This claim is corroborated by the number of incredibly accomplished insomniacs. Despite (or perhaps because of) his insomnia, Marcel Proust completed a seven-volume novel, *Remembrance of Things Past*, mostly in bed. Shakespeare struggled with insomnia and finished almost forty classic plays. Leaders such as Winston Churchill, Benjamin Franklin, and Napoleon Bonaparte likely conducted most of their affairs in a sleep-deprived state.

But what should *you* do when the sleep just won't come? Whether you'd like to embrace the midnight hours or sleep through them, no plan of attack is more manageable and accessible than journaling. As sleep technologist Lauren Butler says, "People with insomnia lie in bed and think, think, think. If they put a notepad by the bed, they can write down all the stuff they're thinking about—the grocery list, pay that bill—so they can release it." Furthermore, according to a widely cited study by James W. Pennebaker and Janel D. Seagal, "Writing about important personal experiences in an emotional way...brings about improvements in mental and physical health." Proven benefits include stress management, strengthened immunity, fewer doctor visits, and improvement in chronic illnesses such as asthma—all of which may improve sleep.

How does this work? Some experts believe organizing experience into a narrative may be beneficial. According to scholarship cited in *Newsweek*, journaling "forces us to transform the ruminations cluttering our minds into coherent stories. Writing about an experience may also dull its emotional impact," which can help you shut off those thoughts long enough to catch some Zs. Journaling may be seen as a way to organize the stuff floating around your conscious brain before the committee of sleep can do its part with the subconscious.

To get the most out of the journaling process, here are a few tips. Experts agree you should try to write quasi-daily, for at least 5–15 minutes. Set up a routine of writing before bedtime (perhaps with some milk and cognac, à la Theodore Roosevelt). Don't critique your writing; just spew. Finally, choose a home for your journal where others won't find it.

Novelist Saul Bellow once declared, "You never have to change anything you got up in the middle of the night to write"—and he won a Nobel Prize. Follow that observation, and not only will you produce written brilliance, but you'll also be on your way to conquering your sleepless nights.

Life is something that happens when you can't get to sleep.

Fran Lebowitz

WHY I CAN'T SLEEP TONIGHT:

_____

_____

_____

_____

_____

_____

_____

_____

_____

_____

_____

_____

_____

_____

_____

_____

_____

_____

WHEN TOMORROW OFFICIALLY BECOMES TODAY:

I realize that from the cradle up I have been like the rest of the race—never quite sane in the night.

Mark Twain

DATE

WHY I CAN'T SLEEP TONIGHT:

_____

_____

_____

_____

_____

_____

_____

_____

_____

_____

_____

_____

_____

_____

_____

_____

WHEN TOMORROW OFFICIALLY BECOMES TODAY:

The last refuge of the insomniac is a sense of superiority to the sleeping world.

Leonard Cohen

WHY I CAN'T SLEEP TONIGHT:

_____

_____

_____

_____

_____

_____

_____

_____

_____

_____

_____

_____

_____

_____

_____

_____

_____

_____

WHEN TOMORROW OFFICIALLY BECOMES TODAY:

I'm for anything that gets you through the night, be it prayer, tranquilizers, or a bottle of Jack Daniel's.

Frank Sinatra

DATE

WHY I CAN'T SLEEP TONIGHT:

_____

_____

_____

_____

_____

_____

_____

_____

_____

_____

_____

_____

_____

_____

_____

_____

WHEN TOMORROW OFFICIALLY BECOMES TODAY:

The average, healthy, well-adjusted adult gets up at seven-thirty in the morning feeling just plain terrible.

Jean Kerr

Many things—such as loving, going to sleep, or behaving unaffectedly—are done worst when we try hardest to do them.

C. S. Lewis

WHY I CAN'T SLEEP TONIGHT:

WHEN TOMORROW OFFICIALLY BECOMES TODAY:

Bed is the best place for reading, thinking, or doing nothing.

Doris Lessing

WHY I CAN'T SLEEP TONIGHT:

WHEN TOMORROW OFFICIALLY BECOMES TODAY:

I hate it when my foot falls asleep during the day, because that means it's going to be up all night.

Steven Wright

WHY I CAN'T SLEEP TONIGHT:

_____

_____

_____

_____

_____

_____

_____

_____

_____

_____

_____

_____

_____

_____

_____

_____

_____

_____

_____

WHEN TOMORROW OFFICIALLY BECOMES TODAY:

A good gulp of hot whiskey at bedtime— it's not very scientific, but it helps.

Sir Alexander Fleming

WHY I CAN'T SLEEP TONIGHT:

_____

_____

_____

_____

_____

_____

_____

_____

_____

_____

_____

_____

_____

_____

_____

_____

WHEN TOMORROW OFFICIALLY BECOMES TODAY:

You know those days when you've got the mean reds ... the blues are because you're getting fat or maybe it's been raining too long. You're sad, that's all. But the mean reds are horrible. You're afraid and you sweat like hell, but you don't know what you're afraid of. Except something bad is going to happen, only you don't know what it is.

Truman Capote

WHY I CAN'T SLEEP TONIGHT:

_____

_____

_____

_____

_____

_____

_____

_____

_____

_____

_____

_____

_____

_____

_____

WHEN TOMORROW OFFICIALLY BECOMES TODAY:

Not being able to
sleep is terrible.
You have the misery
of having partied all
night ... without the
satisfaction.

Lynn Johnston

DATE		

WHY I CAN'T SLEEP TONIGHT:

_____

_____

_____

_____

_____

_____

_____

_____

_____

_____

_____

_____

_____

_____

_____

_____

WHEN TOMORROW OFFICIALLY BECOMES TODAY:

Life is one long process of getting tired.

Samuel Butler

DATE		

WHY I CAN'T SLEEP TONIGHT:

_____

_____

_____

_____

_____

_____

_____

_____

_____

_____

_____

_____

_____

_____

_____

_____

_____

WHEN TOMORROW OFFICIALLY BECOMES TODAY:

No human being believes that any other human being has a right to be in bed when he himself is up.

Robert Lynd

DATE		

WHY I CAN'T SLEEP TONIGHT:

_____

_____

_____

_____

_____

_____

_____

_____

_____

_____

_____

_____

_____

_____

_____

_____

_____

_____

WHEN TOMORROW OFFICIALLY BECOMES TODAY:

A little insomnia
is not without its
value in making
us appreciate sleep,
in throwing a ray
of light upon that
darkness.

Marcel Proust

WHY I CAN'T SLEEP TONIGHT:

_____

_____

_____

_____

_____

_____

_____

_____

_____

_____

_____

_____

_____

_____

_____

_____

WHEN TOMORROW OFFICIALLY BECOMES TODAY:

Character is what you are in the dark.

Dwight L. Moody

DATE

WHY I CAN'T SLEEP TONIGHT:

_____

_____

_____

_____

_____

_____

_____

_____

_____

_____

_____

_____

_____

_____

_____

_____

_____

_____

WHEN TOMORROW OFFICIALLY BECOMES TODAY:

Sometimes I lie awake at night, and I ask, "Where have I gone wrong?" Then a voice says to me, "This is going to take more than one night."

Charles M. Schulz

DATE		

WHY I CAN'T SLEEP TONIGHT:

_____

_____

_____

_____

_____

_____

_____

_____

_____

_____

_____

_____

_____

_____

_____

_____

_____

WHEN TOMORROW OFFICIALLY BECOMES TODAY:

Most people do not consider dawn to be an attractive experience—unless they are still up.

Ellen Goodman

DATE

WHY I CAN'T SLEEP TONIGHT:

_____

_____

_____

_____

_____

_____

_____

_____

_____

_____

_____

_____

_____

_____

_____

_____

_____

WHEN TOMORROW OFFICIALLY BECOMES TODAY:

It seemed to be a necessary ritual that he should prepare himself for sleep by meditating under the solemnity of the night sky...a mysterious transaction between the infinity of the soul and the infinity of the universe.

Victor Hugo

DATE		

WHY I CAN'T SLEEP TONIGHT:

_____

_____

_____

_____

_____

_____

_____

_____

_____

_____

_____

_____

_____

_____

_____

_____

_____

WHEN TOMORROW OFFICIALLY BECOMES TODAY:

In its early stages, insomnia is almost an oasis in which those who have to think or suffer darkly take refuge.

Colette

DATE		

WHY I CAN'T SLEEP TONIGHT:

_____

_____

_____

_____

_____

_____

_____

_____

_____

_____

_____

_____

_____

_____

_____

_____

_____

_____

WHEN TOMORROW OFFICIALLY BECOMES TODAY:

It ain't as bad as you think. It will look better in the morning.

Colin Powell

DATE		

WHY I CAN'T SLEEP TONIGHT:

_____

_____

_____

_____

_____

_____

_____

_____

_____

_____

_____

_____

_____

_____

_____

_____

_____

_____

_____

WHEN TOMORROW OFFICIALLY BECOMES TODAY:

There are times when silence is golden—other times when it is just plain yellow.

Ed Cole

WHY I CAN'T SLEEP TONIGHT:

_____

_____

_____

_____

_____

_____

_____

_____

_____

_____

_____

_____

_____

_____

_____

_____

_____

WHEN TOMORROW OFFICIALLY BECOMES TODAY:

The mind is its own place,
  and in itself

Can make a Heaven of Hell,
  a Hell of Heaven.

John Milton

DATE

WHY I CAN'T SLEEP TONIGHT:

_____

_____

_____

_____

_____

_____

_____

_____

_____

_____

_____

_____

_____

_____

_____

_____

_____

_____

WHEN TOMORROW OFFICIALLY BECOMES TODAY:

Was it only by dreaming or writing that I could find out what I thought?

Joan Didion

DATE

WHY I CAN'T SLEEP TONIGHT:

_____

_____

_____

_____

_____

_____

_____

_____

_____

_____

_____

_____

_____

_____

_____

_____

_____

_____

WHEN TOMORROW OFFICIALLY BECOMES TODAY:

In a real dark night of the soul it is always three o'clock in the morning.

F. Scott Fitzgerald

DATE		

WHY I CAN'T SLEEP TONIGHT:

_____

_____

_____

_____

_____

_____

_____

_____

_____

_____

_____

_____

_____

_____

_____

_____

_____

_____

WHEN TOMORROW OFFICIALLY BECOMES TODAY:

Tonight's forecast: Dark. Continued dark tonight turning to partly light in the morning.

George Carlin

WHY I CAN'T SLEEP TONIGHT:

_____

_____

_____

_____

_____

_____

_____

_____

_____

_____

_____

_____

_____

_____

_____

_____

WHEN TOMORROW OFFICIALLY BECOMES TODAY:

A flock of sheep that
    leisurely pass by,

One after one; the sound of
    rain, and bees

Murmuring; the fall of rivers,
    winds and seas,

Smooth fields, white sheets of
    water, and pure sky;

I have thought of all by turns,
    and yet do lie

Sleepless!

William Wordsworth

WHY I CAN'T SLEEP TONIGHT:

_____
_____
_____
_____
_____
_____
_____
_____
_____
_____
_____
_____
_____
_____
_____
_____
_____
_____

WHEN TOMORROW OFFICIALLY BECOMES TODAY:

How do people go to sleep? I'm afraid I've lost the knack.

Dorothy Parker

WHY I CAN'T SLEEP TONIGHT:

WHEN TOMORROW OFFICIALLY BECOMES TODAY:

Good morning and good luck.

Knock Knock

WHY I CAN'T SLEEP TONIGHT:

_____

_____

_____

_____

_____

_____

_____

_____

_____

_____

_____

_____

_____

_____

_____

_____

_____

_____

WHEN TOMORROW OFFICIALLY BECOMES TODAY:

Don't try to solve serious matters in the middle of the night.

Philip K. Dick

WHEN TOMORROW OFFICIALLY BECOMES TODAY:

WHY I CAN'T SLEEP TONIGHT:

DATE

When I really worry about
something, I don't just fool
around. I even have to go to the
bathroom when I worry about
something. Only, I don't go. I'm
too worried to go. I don't want to
interrupt my worrying to go.

J. D. Salinger

_____

_____

_____

_____

_____

_____

_____

_____

_____

_____

_____

_____

_____

_____

WHY I CAN'T SLEEP TONIGHT:

DATE

Nighttime is really the best time to work. All the ideas are there to be yours because everyone else is asleep.

Catherine O'Hara

WHY I CAN'T SLEEP TONIGHT:

WHEN TOMORROW OFFICIALLY BECOMES TODAY:

It is better
to light
one candle
than to
curse the
darkness.

James Keller

WHEN TOMORROW OFFICIALLY BECOMES TODAY:

_____

_____

_____

_____

_____

_____

_____

_____

_____

_____

_____

_____

_____

_____

_____

_____

WHY I CAN'T SLEEP TONIGHT:

DATE

If you see ten troubles coming down the road, you can be sure that nine will run into the ditch before they reach you.

Calvin Coolidge

WHY I CAN'T SLEEP TONIGHT:

DATE

WHY I CAN'T SLEEP TONIGHT:

_____

_____

_____

_____

_____

_____

_____

_____

_____

_____

_____

_____

_____

_____

_____

_____

_____

_____

WHEN TOMORROW OFFICIALLY BECOMES TODAY:

The worst thing in the world is to try to sleep and not to.

F. Scott Fitzgerald

WHY I CAN'T SLEEP TONIGHT:

_____

_____

_____

_____

_____

_____

_____

_____

_____

_____

_____

_____

_____

_____

_____

WHEN TOMORROW OFFICIALLY BECOMES TODAY:

I have been one acquainted
with the night.

I have walked out in rain—
and back in rain.

I have outwalked the
furthest city light.

Robert Frost

WHY I CAN'T SLEEP TONIGHT:

_____

_____

_____

_____

_____

_____

_____

_____

_____

_____

_____

_____

_____

_____

_____

_____

_____

WHEN TOMORROW OFFICIALLY BECOMES TODAY:

If you're gonna gonna fall apart, do it in your own bedroom.

Margot Kidder

WHY I CAN'T SLEEP TONIGHT:

_____

_____

_____

_____

_____

_____

_____

_____

_____

_____

_____

_____

_____

_____

_____

_____

_____

WHEN TOMORROW OFFICIALLY BECOMES TODAY:

Fasten your seatbelts.
It's going to be a
bumpy night.

Joseph L. Mankiewicz

WHY I CAN'T SLEEP TONIGHT:

_____

_____

_____

_____

_____

_____

_____

_____

_____

_____

_____

_____

_____

_____

_____

_____

_____

WHEN TOMORROW OFFICIALLY BECOMES TODAY:

Brave captain, why are the wicked so strong? How do the angels get to sleep when the devil leaves the porch light on?

Tom Waits

DATE		

WHY I CAN'T SLEEP TONIGHT:

_____

_____

_____

_____

_____

_____

_____

_____

_____

_____

_____

_____

_____

_____

_____

_____

_____

WHEN TOMORROW OFFICIALLY BECOMES TODAY:

Whoever thinks of going to bed before twelve o'clock is a scoundrel.

Samuel Johnson

WHY I CAN'T SLEEP TONIGHT:

_____

_____

_____

_____

_____

_____

_____

_____

_____

_____

_____

_____

_____

_____

_____

_____

_____

_____

WHEN TOMORROW OFFICIALLY BECOMES TODAY:

Sleeplessness is a desert without vegetation or inhabitants.

Jessamyn West

WHY I CAN'T SLEEP TONIGHT:

_____

_____

_____

_____

_____

_____

_____

_____

_____

_____

_____

_____

_____

_____

_____

_____

_____

WHEN TOMORROW OFFICIALLY BECOMES TODAY:

There are nights when the wolves are silent and only the moon howls.

George Carlin

DATE		

WHY I CAN'T SLEEP TONIGHT:

_____

_____

_____

_____

_____

_____

_____

_____

_____

_____

_____

_____

_____

_____

_____

_____

_____

WHEN TOMORROW OFFICIALLY BECOMES TODAY:

The best cure for insomnia is to get a lot of sleep.

W. C. Fields

DATE		

WHY I CAN'T SLEEP TONIGHT:

_____

_____

_____

_____

_____

_____

_____

_____

_____

_____

_____

_____

_____

_____

_____

_____

_____

WHEN TOMORROW OFFICIALLY BECOMES TODAY:

Oh, the nerves, the nerves; the mysteries of this machine called Man! Oh, the little that unhinges it; poor creatures that we are!

Charles Dickens

A man's subconscious self is not the ideal companion. It lurks for the greater part of his life in some dark den of its own, hidden away, and emerges only to taunt and deride and increase the misery of a miserable hour.

P. G. Wodehouse

WHY I CAN'T SLEEP TONIGHT:

WHEN TOMORROW OFFICIALLY BECOMES TODAY:

Tomorrow night is nothing but one long sleepless wrestle with yesterday's omissions and regrets.

William Faulkner

DATE		

WHY I CAN'T SLEEP TONIGHT:

_____

_____

_____

_____

_____

_____

_____

_____

_____

_____

_____

_____

_____

_____

_____

_____

WHEN TOMORROW OFFICIALLY BECOMES TODAY:

It's crazy how you can get yourself in a mess sometimes and not even be able to think about it with any sense and yet not be able to think about anything else.

Stanley Kubrick

WHY I CAN'T SLEEP TONIGHT:

_____

_____

_____

_____

_____

_____

_____

_____

_____

_____

_____

_____

_____

_____

_____

_____

_____

WHEN TOMORROW OFFICIALLY BECOMES TODAY:

I'll sleep when I'm dead.

Warren Zevon

WHY I CAN'T SLEEP TONIGHT:

WHEN TOMORROW OFFICIALLY BECOMES TODAY:

We spend our midday sweat,
  our midnight oil;

We tire the night in thought,
  the day in toil.

Francis Quarles

WHY I CAN'T SLEEP TONIGHT:

_____

_____

_____

_____

_____

_____

_____

_____

_____

_____

_____

_____

_____

_____

_____

_____

WHEN TOMORROW OFFICIALLY BECOMES TODAY:

You never have to change anything you got up in the middle of the night to write.

Saul Bellow

DATE

WHY I CAN'T SLEEP TONIGHT:

_____

_____

_____

_____

_____

_____

_____

_____

_____

_____

_____

_____

_____

_____

_____

_____

_____

_____

_____

WHEN TOMORROW OFFICIALLY BECOMES TODAY:

If you can't sleep, then get up and do something instead of lying there worrying. It's the worry that gets you, not the lack of sleep.

Dale Carnegie

WHY I CAN'T SLEEP TONIGHT:

WHEN TOMORROW OFFICIALLY BECOMES TODAY:

There is a drowsy state, between sleeping and waking, when you dream more in five minutes with your eyes half open, and yourself half conscious of everything that is passing around you, than you would in five nights with your eyes fast closed and your senses wrapt in perfect unconsciousness.

Charles Dickens

DATE

WHY I CAN'T SLEEP TONIGHT:

_____

_____

_____

_____

_____

_____

_____

_____

_____

_____

_____

_____

_____

_____

_____

_____

_____

_____

WHEN TOMORROW OFFICIALLY BECOMES TODAY:

You can't stand up to the night until you understand what's hiding in its shadows.

Charles de Lint

DATE

WHY I CAN'T SLEEP TONIGHT:

_____

_____

_____

_____

_____

_____

_____

_____

_____

_____

_____

_____

_____

_____

_____

_____

_____

_____

WHEN TOMORROW OFFICIALLY BECOMES TODAY:

Sleeping is no mean art: for its sake one must stay awake all day.

Friedrich Nietzsche

DATE

WHY I CAN'T SLEEP TONIGHT:

_____

_____

_____

_____

_____

_____

_____

_____

_____

_____

_____

_____

_____

_____

_____

_____

_____

_____

WHEN TOMORROW OFFICIALLY BECOMES TODAY:

DATE

WHY I CAN'T SLEEP TONIGHT:

_____

_____

_____

_____

_____

_____

_____

_____

_____

_____

_____

_____

_____

_____

_____

_____

_____

WHEN TOMORROW OFFICIALLY BECOMES TODAY:

I told the doctor I was overtired, anxiety ridden, compulsively active, constantly depressed, with recurring fits of paranoia. Turns out I'm normal.

Jules Feiffer

WHY I CAN'T SLEEP TONIGHT:

_____

_____

_____

_____

_____

_____

_____

_____

_____

_____

_____

_____

_____

_____

_____

_____

WHEN TOMORROW OFFICIALLY BECOMES TODAY:

There are two types of people in this world: good and bad. The good sleep better, but the bad seem to enjoy the waking hours much more.

Woody Allen

DATE

WHY I CAN'T SLEEP TONIGHT:

_____

_____

_____

_____

_____

_____

_____

_____

_____

_____

_____

_____

_____

_____

_____

_____

WHEN TOMORROW OFFICIALLY BECOMES TODAY:

How much pain have cost us the evils which have never happened!

Thomas Jefferson

WHY I CAN'T SLEEP TONIGHT:

_____

_____

_____

_____

_____

_____

_____

_____

_____

_____

_____

_____

_____

_____

_____

_____

_____

WHEN TOMORROW OFFICIALLY BECOMES TODAY:

A ruffled mind makes a restless pillow.

Charlotte Brontë

WHY I CAN'T SLEEP TONIGHT:

_____

_____

_____

_____

_____

_____

_____

_____

_____

_____

_____

_____

_____

_____

_____

_____

_____

WHEN TOMORROW OFFICIALLY BECOMES TODAY:

What hath night to do with sleep?

John Milton

WHY I CAN'T SLEEP TONIGHT:

_____

_____

_____

_____

_____

_____

_____

_____

_____

_____

_____

_____

_____

_____

_____

_____

_____

_____

WHEN TOMORROW OFFICIALLY BECOMES TODAY:

The heights by great men reached
  and kept

Were not attained by sudden flight,

But they, while their companions slept,

Were toiling upward in the night.

Henry Wadsworth Longfellow

WHY I CAN'T SLEEP TONIGHT:

_____

_____

_____

_____

_____

_____

_____

_____

_____

_____

_____

_____

_____

_____

_____

_____

_____

_____

WHEN TOMORROW OFFICIALLY BECOMES TODAY:

To be too conscious is an illness—
a real thoroughgoing illness.

Fyodor Dostoyevsky

WHY I CAN'T SLEEP TONIGHT:

_____

_____

_____

_____

_____

_____

_____

_____

_____

_____

_____

_____

_____

_____

_____

_____

_____

_____

WHEN TOMORROW OFFICIALLY BECOMES TODAY:

It is one of life's bitterest truths that bedtime so often arrives just when things are really getting interesting.

Lemony Snicket

DATE		

WHY I CAN'T SLEEP TONIGHT:

_____

_____

_____

_____

_____

_____

_____

_____

_____

_____

_____

_____

_____

_____

_____

WHEN TOMORROW OFFICIALLY BECOMES TODAY:

Hello darkness, my old friend
I've come to talk with you again.

Paul Simon

WHY I CAN'T SLEEP TONIGHT:

_____

_____

_____

_____

_____

_____

_____

_____

_____

_____

_____

_____

_____

_____

_____

_____

WHEN TOMORROW OFFICIALLY BECOMES TODAY:

I often think that the night
is more alive and more richly
colored than the day.

Vincent van Gogh

DATE

WHY I CAN'T SLEEP TONIGHT:

_____

_____

_____

_____

_____

_____

_____

_____

_____

_____

_____

_____

_____

_____

_____

_____

WHEN TOMORROW OFFICIALLY BECOMES TODAY:

Sleep, that deplorable curtailment of the joy of life.

Virginia Woolf

WHY I CAN'T SLEEP TONIGHT:

_____

_____

_____

_____

_____

_____

_____

_____

_____

_____

_____

_____

_____

_____

_____

_____

_____

_____

WHEN TOMORROW OFFICIALLY BECOMES TODAY:

When you have insomnia, you're never really asleep, and you're never really awake.

Chuck Palahniuk

DATE		

WHY I CAN'T SLEEP TONIGHT:

_____

_____

_____

_____

_____

_____

_____

_____

_____

_____

_____

_____

_____

_____

_____

_____

WHEN TOMORROW OFFICIALLY BECOMES TODAY:

I haven't been to sleep for over a year. That's why I go to bed early. One needs more rest if one doesn't sleep.

Evelyn Waugh

WHY I CAN'T SLEEP TONIGHT:

_____

_____

_____

_____

_____

_____

_____

_____

_____

_____

_____

_____

_____

_____

_____

_____

_____

_____

WHEN TOMORROW OFFICIALLY BECOMES TODAY:

When I feel well and in a good humour, or when I am taking a drive or walking after a good meal, or in the night when I cannot sleep, thoughts crowd into my mind as easily as you could wish.

Wolfgang Amadeus Mozart

WHY I CAN'T SLEEP TONIGHT:

_____

_____

_____

_____

_____

_____

_____

_____

_____

_____

_____

_____

_____

_____

_____

_____

_____

_____

WHEN TOMORROW OFFICIALLY BECOMES TODAY:

We are dying from overthinking.
We are slowly killing ourselves by
thinking about everything. Think.
Think. Think. You can never trust
the human mind anyway.
It's a death trap.

Anthony Hopkins

WHY I CAN'T SLEEP TONIGHT:

_____

_____

_____

_____

_____

_____

_____

_____

_____

_____

_____

_____

_____

_____

_____

_____

_____

_____

WHEN TOMORROW OFFICIALLY BECOMES TODAY:

The summer demands and takes
   away too much,

But night, the reserved, the reticent,
   gives more than it takes.

John Ashbery

WHY I CAN'T SLEEP TONIGHT:

DATE

Sleep is the most moronic
fraternity in the world,
with the heaviest dues
and the crudest rituals.

Vladimir Nabokov

_____

_____

_____

_____

_____

_____

_____

_____

_____

_____

_____

_____

_____

_____

_____

_____

WHY I CAN'T SLEEP TONIGHT:

DATE

Drag your thoughts
away from your
troubles—by the ears,
by the heels, or any
other way, so you
can manage it.

Mark Twain

WHY I CAN'T SLEEP TONIGHT:

DATE

So dear night the
half of life is,

And the fairest
half indeed.

Johann Wolfgang von Goethe

WHEN TOMORROW OFFICIALLY BECOMES TODAY:

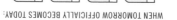

WHY I CAN'T SLEEP TONIGHT:

Dawn, *n.* The time when men of reason go to bed.

Ambrose Bierce

WHEN TOMORROW OFFICIALLY BECOMES TODAY:

_____

_____

_____

_____

_____

_____

_____

_____

_____

_____

_____

_____

_____

_____

_____

_____

_____

WHY I CAN'T SLEEP TONIGHT:

DATE

From restless thoughts, that,
like a deadly swarm
Of hornets arm'd, no sooner
found alone,
But rush upon me thronging.

John Milton

WHEN TOMORROW OFFICIALLY BECOMES TODAY:

_____

_____

_____

_____

_____

_____

_____

_____

_____

_____

_____

_____

_____

_____

WHY I CAN'T SLEEP TONIGHT:

DATE

Don't start me talking
I could talk all night
My mind goes sleepwalking
While I'm putting the world to right.

Elvis Costello

WHEN TOMORROW OFFICIALLY BECOMES TODAY:

_____

_____

_____

_____

_____

_____

_____

_____

_____

_____

_____

_____

_____

_____

_____

_____

_____

WHY I CAN'T SLEEP TONIGHT:

DATE

Most glorious night!
Thou wert not sent
for slumber!

Lord Byron

WHEN TOMORROW OFFICIALLY BECOMES TODAY:

_____

_____

_____

_____

_____

_____

_____

_____

_____

_____

_____

_____

_____

_____

_____

WHY I CAN'T SLEEP TONIGHT:

DATE

Stop worrying—nobody gets out of this world alive.

Clive James

WHEN TOMORROW OFFICIALLY BECOMES TODAY:

WHY I CAN'T SLEEP TONIGHT:

DATE

...and so to bed.

Samuel Pepys